CW00386352

"Always stay kind, curious and embrace your imagination"

For my sister Charlotte, daughter Artemis and Goddaughter Edie

First published in Great Britain in 2021 by Fluffy Heart Publishing.

A CIP catalogue record for this book is available from the British Library
ISBN 978-1-9997841-2-6
Printed in Lithuania

The Squirrels of Hyde Park

By Emelie Salford

Trendy Notting Hill Joe

The boy is so cool he simply can't decide which trend to follow. He brushes his oversized Mohican style quiff 100 times a day or more to accentuate his cheekbones. Lately Joe has been seen scavenging for leftover spray paint cans. His aim is to take over the London graffiti scene, the boy is on a mission, never sits down. There's no time to waste for the squirrel who has taken on the stage name "The Hurricane", and he won't rule out any wall.

His motto is: "Stay strong and bring it on!"

KONST

Sophisticated South Kensington Lydia and George

This couple can't get enough of the local antiquarian bookdealers. When the human race aren't watching, they're in there, ready to read and further their knowledge.

Due to miniscule muscle mass they're unable to bring the books home so they've adopted a speed reading technique. They can master 5 books in one hour in fact.

lonely planet

A ROGUE ECON
EXPLORES T
SIDE OF EV

12 RULE

MICHIO
KAKU

LONDON

ROPARDS

by Emelie Salford

Party Pooper Paddington Prudence

She is obsessed with knitting tail warmers from human male chest hair and just cannot face socialising with the rest of the squirrel race, she's just too busy knitting away night and day!

What's rather curious about Prudence is that she seems so shy and well behaved, when actually every night she climbs through letterboxes, then delicately detects the sleeping humans in their beds.

No Junk Mail

On her back she carries a bag that she's previously knitted and this will serve as her container for new knitting material. Her technique consists of movements as quick as lightning, picking approximately 10 chest hairs from each male human.

Just enough hair is plucked in order to fit a ¾ burnt down cake candle into her little bag – knitting during night requires light!

Why she has specialised in human hair is quite curious but I suppose, just like humans, squirrels are fascinated by wearing other species natural textures. It is all obvious.

Casino Crazed Queensway Ray

From behind the jukebox he follows every skilled dance move performed by the humans on the fluorescent dance floor. It's one of those game dance floors where you have to move your feet in time to the lit up squares on the floor. Ray can sit and watch the guys for hours. He is desperate to participate but that's being unrealistic! His small legs just can't stretch that far apart! Ray is a squirrel not a human, that's a fact!

Ray's favourite joint, as you've probably guessed, is the Queensway Game Centre. A venue that never lets you down when you want to go car racing, ice skating, dancing, bowling and of course gambling. Now, that's where Ray comes alive, he is called 'the Boy with the golden pouch' and there's a reason for it.

Whenever someone puts a pound into the jackpot machine, grey furry paws become braced and eyes light up, awaiting that luxurious rain of coins. Now and then a shimmering coin might slip the human hand and then, ready, pumped up and attentive, Ray is in ready position, he quickly grabs hold of it and safely stores it in his pouch. He is relying on income for his weekly dose of caramel covered almonds. Ray has a sweet tooth and he doesn't deny it.

Last week he had to settle for one bag of the goodies in exchange for a knitted tail warmer that he had bought from Paddington Prudence who wisely spent her money on toothpicks to serve as knitting needles. Toothpicks are difficult to come by, this Prudence has realised from her nightly visits searching for male chest hair and burnt down candles.

Joker
POKER

Fashion Flamboyant Knightsbridge Chloe

Addicted to the Harvey Nichols's window display, Chloe visits the site every night so she doesn't need to share the view. It's calm, quiet and created just for her.

Chloe is seen daily, walking down Sloane Street, peering at the human fashion victims marching above her. She takes frequent notes of what's the latest in fashion and if she's lucky, someone from the human race might drop something sparkly and beautiful. Her moto is: "If it's on the ground, it's yours to be found."

Clever Chloe's home is a beautiful cave of curiosities. From the ceiling hangs a brooch with the precious stones facing downwards, just like a chandelier, something she'd previously seen in the window of Harvey Nichols. The floor is tiled in sequins which she'd plucked off a scarf that she'd found outside Prada, halfway down Sloane Street.

She is widely known for her innovative sense of fashion and when her fellow squirrels need a helping hand with spicing up their homes, they call on clever Chloe.

Health and safety conscious High Street Kensington Conrad

He has taken it upon himself to man the unmanned red sentry hut on the human subway trains. It was the closest call to becoming a Queen's Guard, something he'd always dreamt of.

Conrad is constantly on the lookout for anything suspicious that needs reporting. He had heard on the speakers: "See it. Say it. Sort it!" and this he lives by.

The humans mostly think of him as a little lost toy, propped up in the corner of the train, but how little do they know! Suddenly Conrad would spring up, tap a human on the foot, point to and remind them about their left behind bag. Conrad is alert that's for sure!

Slick Sense of Speed Bachelor Barnaby of Lancaster Gate

There is no question about it, if someone knows about cars and speed, it's Barnaby. From the day he was born he possessed the passion and he is mighty proud of it.

For as long as he can remember his fantasy has been to construct a miniature burgundy coloured Ferrari.

Well, in order to construct this miniature but yet monstrous beauty, Barnaby had to do some serious investigating, sneaking around car shops and invisibly dropping in on Ferrari Dealers'. For ten years he has been disguised as a car-mechanic-mascot, sitting in on University Engineering courses.

By now he would most likely be a Professor in the History and Engineering of Ferrari Cars, if he was a human that is.

One occasion that he'll never miss is the Earl's Court Car Fair. This is a date to celebrate! Barnaby will make sure that his fur is well groomed and that he has his note pad, a tape measure and a sharpened pencil, ready to write. New information is like gold dust, this Barnaby knows too well.

Green Clawed Gardener Holland Park Cliff

Cliff adopted his Christian name from the inspirational Cliffs of Dover: the mighty, white muses created by nature.

Cliff is a guy you can rely on, hardworking and loves to help out whenever and wherever he can. There is no limit to Cliff's generosity.

It is likely the trigger to his remarkable gift of giving came into practice the day Cliff woke up from a two-week coma after being attacked by two pugs.

They tossed him up in the air and played with him as if he was made of velour, like some kind of toy without feelings. He fell to the ground and suffered a concussion. He knew something had gone very wrong when his vision played tricks on him and he saw multiple tree surgeons floating on branches in the sky above .

Luckily Prudence happened to walk past, ready to act! She rapidly took out her knitting gear and started to work on a harness made of human chest hair, one that she could wear and connect to her suffering friend. Cliff was carefully dragged by Prudence into her modest home in Paddington where he was comfortably placed in a knitted hammock.

All his friends expressed their love and deepest concerns for their fellow squirrel. He was now in need of love! Meanwhile, Lancaster Gate Barnaby lived close to Paddington Prudence so he offered her his help to care for Cliff.

Prudence wouldn't naturally hang out with her fellow squirrels but this rather unfortunate incident had funnily enough brought new light and excitement into her life.

As Barnaby whispered into her well groomed ear that he would be the happiest squirrel in the whole world if she would knit him a red tail warmer, Prudence's face hair was raised in a prickly formation indicating a charmed blush. She had spent the winter blushing every time she had spotted him climbing a tree or storing nuts (which he did almost religiously).

After 15 minutes of small talk the moment of passion was unavoidable as their soft noses met in a tender kiss. Prudence couldn't believe it, this was an experience better than knitting, unbelievable!

A squeak of joy was heard from across the room; Love had brought Cliff back! "I'm here to stay! Long live Love."

This miraculous incident of passion had brought back memories for Cliff of Rose, the precious princess living in the brick house in Holland Park. During the past year Cliff had passed her door on the way to work, hoping that he would accidentally bump into her but it had never happened.

The first memory of Rose was a precious one, it was in 2005 when Cliff attended the Chelsea Flower Show. A certain scent, foreign to Cliff's delicate nose guided him into the heart of the building and there she was, Rose, the most precious creature, creating topiary rose bushes in the shape of animals. Cliff noted her devotion to detail as she swapped between the different sized clippers.

What if the two of them could meet up and discuss gardening ideas? What a wonderful thought! Cliff's realisation about Rose gave him the courage to pack up his home and plan his proposal. He had a vision to transform his home into an art gallery, a place to socialise and make new friends.

One thing he'd realised following his rather unpleasant experience in the park, was the value of good friendships and never to underestimate the power of the squirrel community.

Now that he had been given a second chance in life, he realised the importance of listening to his heart and trusting his intuition, and what better way than to surprise the dream goddess of Holland Park?

Cliff was eager to carry out his plan in the name of Love. He had spent the whole day filling his baskets with beautiful flowers. He then carried them to the brick house on Portland Road, and quietly began tiling a floral path.

The idea was for Rose to wake up in the morning to the alluring scent of jasmine, rose and lily of the valley! She would discover the floral path that would guide her to Cliff's house.

The following morning all went according to plan and Rose was mighty flattered. She decided to gather the flowers as she followed the winding path, and one by one she stitched them together, creating the fabric that would form her magical dress.

Cliff whispered, "Let your mighty forces lead her here, let her not be far but near."

There she stood outside his house at 8pm dressed in the finest of Floral Couture and behind her a train of stitched, petals. Her beauty! The scent! The magical moment was simply overpowering and Cliff was in a silent state of shock. In a squeaky, weak voice he simply uttered the words, "Will you marry me?"

A rather unexpected question for Rose but in the excitement she just couldn't conceal her beautiful, delicate smile and with a happy little voice she replied, "Yes! Yes!"

There it was, the happiest moment of their lives! The petal-path of love lead them to tying the knot.

Their evening wedding reception was held at the 2-Niche Stage in Kensington Gardens and The Nutsters were the main band. There was dancing, singing and bathing in the fountain until the early hours! The joy was infectious and all the animals in the park joined in. What a night!

On Sunday mornings the lake in Hyde Park is crowded with luxury yachts manoeuvred by humans and occasionally their miniature lookalikes have a go at stirring the boats.

Rose and Cliff spent part of their honeymoon on such a yacht, well two hours of their honeymoon to be precise. Not exactly a five star yacht experience but it did have all the basic mod cons.

It was a rather pleasant ride until the miniature lookalike had his turn to steer the boat causing it to capsize. In a state of panic the couple had to swim and seek protection on the back of a swan.

They agreed that this was a far superior ride, both in terms of comfort and speed. Nature rules!

As the couple were enjoying their honeymoon ride across the lake they sang: "Let's embrace a greener, cleaner world"

The sensation of love had rubbed off on Barnaby. He called it a lot of love nonsense but little did he know how positive the impact had been on him.

This was a guy keen to hang out at the local pub showing off his burgundy coloured motor, that he'd constructed following endless educational Engineering seminars listening in, disguised as a toy squirrel mechanic.

However now, his thoughts were purely fixed on Paddington Prudence. He was mesmerised by the caring qualities she'd displayed while caring for Cliff. She was simply a saint, worth fighting for.

In the past, Ray frequently enjoyed a Bellini or a Dry Martini at Nutfellas in South Kensington.

A recent visit had given him the ground breaking idea of inventing a friendly enterprise between squirrels and humans. He invited his fellow squirrels to discuss his grand plans.

Life as a Hyde Park Squirrel was rather wonderful but they all wanted to adopt the glamourous human style of living. Their plan was to build a luxury spa, leaving behind them their days of bathing in the human drinking fountain. It is not so much fun to wash your bits and bobs when a king sized poodle approaches, thirsty for a drink.

The time had also come to build a Yoga Centre, a Dotted-Game-Dance-Floor, a UFO-looking trick-a-treat-Time-Machine, a Recording Studio, a Unisex-Fur-Dresser an Art Gallery and a Country House retreat. In order to construct the above venues the squirrels had to get their small furry hands on materials sold by the humans.

Sharing innovative marketing ideas, the squirrels came up with products required by humans.

SOUTH KENSINGTON

A friendly commerce was created and nurtured between squirrels and humans. It was time to make use of the human knowledge. The time had come for fair-trading without physically fading away. Through teamwork they would achieve comfort.

The squirrels all settled on their own innovative tasks in order to raise the money needed to trade with the humans.

Paddington Prudence and Lancaster Gate Barnaby were in charge of constructing a local Spa with an Olympic sized pool; well in squirrel measurements that is.

In order to get their miniscule hands on marble from Florence and water from the springs of Lourdes the squirrels had to be very dedicated and disciplined.

Paddington Prudence now had to adapt her products to the human need and what better way than to collect the fellow squirrels' fur during shedding season and together with Barnaby make the finest of artists' paint brushes ever to be seen!

The products had to be transported to the local art shops and, Oh boy! The portfolio was heavy but luckily, the couple could rely on the burgundy coloured motor.

The couple had commissioned Notting Hill Joe to create an external mural and they were pleased with the sleek outcome. Joe's design was out of this world - really the talk of the town.

Knightsbridge Chloe was determined to build a Yoga Centre.

Her dedicated duties consisted of dressing up as a Butterfly-Fairy (like the one she'd seen in the window display at Harvey Nics), and showing off her different yoga moves. The lotus position was a clear favourite.

Paddington Prudence had knitted her a little pouch, where humans could leave a coin or two.

Her joints were getting so flexible that she was by now able to go down into 'the splits' – a move that generated lots of income.

Ray had set high goals for the future luxury village and he was left rather exhausted.

The boy with the golden pouch had spent endless hours collecting coins, hiding under the jackpot machine in order to realise his dream.

Ray had mastered building his dream dance machine, a replica of the lit up dance floor at Queensway Game Centre - now fit for squirrel measures!

Would it get much better than this?

Me Your Move
how Me Your Move
how Me Your Mo

Ingenious Ray had also reconstructed a UFO-looking arcade machine that he had previously fallen in love with.

Ray's plan was that the human race would come and put nuts through the coin-hole, expecting to win the fluffy squirrel inside, but HA! How could they possibly? There was no way that Ray would fall out through the prize-dispenser, he was way too fat for that!

Ray had his own secret, disguised door, seamlessly invisible to the human eye.

Day in and day out he would sit in his Earth based UFO - arcade gadget, munch on nuts and plan his trip to Outer Space, possibly to the Planet of Electronic-Love-Games, where he would find his Dream-Date. He had it all sussed out!

CHANGE
INSERT PEANUTS AND THE
SQUIRREL WILL FALL OUT

Joe had always wanted to be a Fur-Dresser and his dream was to set up 'The Mohican', a friendly Unisex Salon. One thing he would be able to offer was fur extensions. Imagine; now everyone had a chance to look like him!

Prudence had offered to give Joe the fur-left-overs from her manufacturing of artists' paint brushes.

The Nutsters had already made appointments for fur extensions. Being in a band and soon Managers of a Recording Studio, they now needed to create a new image, somehow make a statement about their Coolness and what better way than to make wild, wicked coloured fur extensions?

In order to realise his dream; "The Mohican" Joe urgently needed the finest of fur-products. In exchange for high quality, professional shampoo, conditioner, mousse and miniature scissors, Joe had agreed to come in twice a week to a famous Mayfair Hairdresser in order to sort out the eyebrow tinting mixture and apply it to the human eyebrow. Well luckily he didn't have to colour a whole human set of hair – imagine how long that would take Joe!

JOE'S
MOHICAN
HAIRDRESSER

HAIR EXTENSION
SPECIALIST

BEFORE

AFTER

The Nutsters had now changed their stage name to: The Tuftsters and during four weeks they'd been practicing cover tunes – something the human race could relate to. Their repertoire consisted of 'Money, money, money' by Abba, 'Money makes the world go round' by Liza Minnelli and 'Money' by Pink Floyd.

The songs were performed daily at the '2-Niche Stage' in Hyde Park. The Tuftsters aim was to raise enough income to be able to invest in a microphone bought from the humans that could be tapped in to the electric sockets belonging to the human race. Just imagine the audio force, quite a sound-blasting system!

From one dismantled human drum ten squirrel ones could be created and one dismantled guitar would supply the band with eight guitars, both ordinary and base guitars. The Tuftsters were very eager to see the day when their goal was reached; a complete recording studio with all the gadgets.

THE TUFTSTERS
THE
TUFTSTERS

Cliff's old house had now been turned into an art gallery and a welcoming community space where all the squirrels could come together and socialise.

The art on the walls mainly addressed the human race and their identity issues.

Health and safety aware Conrad had expressed to his fellow squirrels a deep concern about Ralph, the new kid in town who appeared to have an obsession with loo rolls.

He was one to watch, in fact he was No 1 on Conrad's health and safety hazard list.

FOAM

Loo paper fanatic Gloucester Road Ralph

Was constantly on a mission adding to his collection, he simply couldn't have enough of the padded rolls.

Once, when asked about his collection, or rather obsession, his answer was:
"Well, if we are to follow the human style of living, this is what they seem to be doing, during challenging times"

Do not
touch

CCTV
IN OPERATION

Rose & Cliff as expected, decided to cut animal shapes from bushes and sell them as miniatures to human bonsai tree dealers in order to raise a budget to build their dream country retreat in the Cotswolds. A place where everyone would be welcome!

Rose managed to cut about six animal shaped bushes a day, five of them being sheep-shaped. A shape, which obviously appealed to the human eye. Why? Well, maybe because it makes City People believe that they are out and about in the Countryside.

By now the couple had trimmed so many sheep that it had affected their sleep. Both Rose and Cliff would count sheep in their sleep and the sleep deprivation had sadly become evident in their latest collection.

They asked themselves "why wasn't the human race interested in their latest stock of sheep?" Well, the shape was no longer fluffy and cuddly, it now instead bore an uncanny resemblance to the 'Chinese Naked Dog'.

After much thought, Cliff came up with the genius idea, of borrowing Barnaby's car and driving the newly cut stock to Chop-san, the Chinese bonsai dealer in Mayfair.

Believe it or not! Chop-san was so impressed with the new exquisitely trimmed collection, that he bought the lot and put in an order for a hundred more.

Misfortune can sometimes lead to fortune!

This Cliff learnt from spending time, tucked away, with a concusion, following the unfortunate incident with two pugs but later liaising with the beautiful Rose, the Love of his Life.

Something so frightening would lead to something so frightfully exciting – a new beginning!

Ray is a keen daydreamer, you often find him on the railings where he pretends that he's steering his ship towards exciting destinations!

Never underestimate
the power of daydreaming!